To all of those who need an extra piece to the puzzle in finding Jesus and to my mom who shared this special journey with me. I love you -J

ISBN: 979-8-9866633-1-9

For more books, visit us online at pray2jesuswithjenisys.com

# Can Jesus Really Hear My Prayers?

JENISYS OLIVER-JOSEPH

# Can Jesus really hear my prayers?

Yes, I know some people can listen to our prayers.
But can Jesus?

Some people who might be listening could be our parents, church members, or even those we just pray in front of.

But how can only Jesus hear me?

I'm all the way down here on Earth.

Does He have really big ears like an elephant?

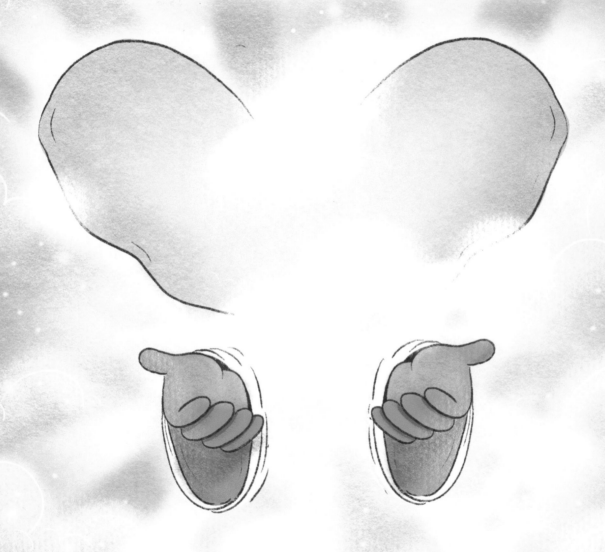

Can He only hear me as the sun rises?

Can I pray on the playground?

Can Jesus really hear me praying
while I'm sitting in traffic?

Maybe He can't because of the beeping horns.

What if Jesus can only hear me
during the winter season?

Since the snow will be quiet while it's falling.

Is Jesus able to hear me praying while there's a storm?

I wonder if He would be able to hear
my prayers if I was in the hospital.

Can He hear me praying in the living
room or maybe in the kitchen?

Or do the clanging dishes or humming vacuum when my mom is cleaning the house make too much noise for Him to hear?

Is Jesus able to hear me praying while I have my favorite TV show playing?

Or should I turn down the volume or mute
the TV so that He can hear me clearly?

I bet Jesus can definitely
hear me praying in the library!

No, of course not! Jesus can listen to us anywhere and everywhere.

He listens to us through His Holy Spirit.

So, it does not matter where we are, what we are doing, or how loud or quiet it is.

Yes! Jesus can still hear us.

Yes! Jesus can really hear my prayers.
Amen.

# About the Author

Jenisys Oliver-Joseph stands firm in 1 Thessalonians 5:17 and is known for letting her little light shine wherever she travels. At the age of 4, she developed a strong relationship with Jesus. In 2020, she began sharing her love for Jesus with others by sharing online prayer and encouragement videos. She also heavily engaged in beautification projects throughout her community during this time. Jenisys has self-trained in gymnastics, ballet, and yoga. Her ultimate dream is to make it into the Olympics. She also loves painting with her family, swimming and learning new languages.

Discover more about Jenisys at pray2jesuswithjenisys.com
and subscribe to her YouTube channel, Pray 2 Jesus with Jenisys.

pray2jesuswithjenisys          pray2jesuswithjenisys          pray2jesuswithjenisys

Lightning Source UK Ltd.
Milton Keynes UK
UKHW050500080223
416583UK00003B/75